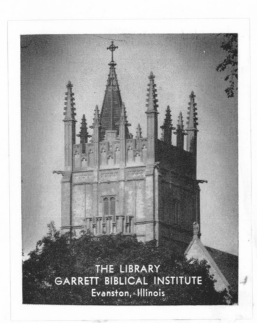

Dear Boys and Girls,

All through the years and all around the world men and women and boys and girls have thought about God and about the world he has planned. Sometimes people have written their thoughts, and other people have read them.

The Bible is a very special book, because it tells, more than any other book, about God and about his plan for the world and for people.

Some parts of the Bible boys and girls read for themselves. Some parts of it parents and teachers and religious leaders read to boys and girls. Some parts of it are written in a language that boys and girls find hard to understand. They need storytellers and writers and artists to help them listen to some of the thoughts in the Bible.

In this book a writer helps boys and girls to understand a great poem in the Bible by putting it into simpler words. And an artist helps them understand it by drawing pictures.

The Bible poem is called a Psalm. It tells about God and the world he has planned. The thoughts of the Psalm are very big ones. But they are thoughts that often come to boys and girls.

The Psalm in this book is based upon Psalm 104 in the Bible. Perhaps one day you would like to find it in your Bible!

Mary Alice Jones

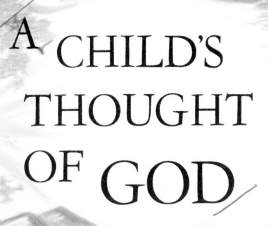

A CHILD'S THOUGHT OF GOD

A Poem Based on Psalm 104

by HELLEN DRUMMOND ASHER

Illustrated by DOROTHY GRIDER

RAND McNALLY & COMPANY

NEW YORK   CHICAGO   SAN FRANCISCO

I want to say

"Thank you," God!

I feel how great you are!

I close my eyes
   and think of you,
   beautiful and shining
   among the stars
   and all around me!

Sometimes you seem near me,

like my mother,

covered with her

quilted bathrobe

as she reads the Bible to me.

Sometimes I feel you
close to me,
like the wind
coming to fly my kite
as I ride my tricycle.

When the sky is fiery red

as the sun goes down

at evening,

I know that you are there,

making everything beautiful

and reminding me

that you are very great.

I wonder how
  you planned the earth,
  dear God.
It feels so firm and safe.
I chase my ball,
  play marbles,
  run and jump and swing,
  and always your earth
  is sure beneath my feet.

The Bible says that long ago
the waters covered the earth
like a big ocean.

Then the mountains grew high,
and soft valleys came between,
while the waters sank low into
the deep cracks of the earth,
as you planned for them to do.

I love to cup my hands

and drink

at the spring

on the mountainside.

When I am very still,

I see a baby fawn

stick out its tongue

for the bubbles of water.

I hear the birds singing

in the branches above me.

I have such fun

on my grandfather's farm—

in my bare feet

I feel the dewy grass

of the pasture;

I tickle the sides

of old bossy cow;

I watch the farmers

run the plows

and big machines

that cultivate the land

to help the grain to grow.

In the kitchen my grandmother
kneads the bread
with her hands.

Which smells better,
the fresh bread
from the open door
or the ocean's spray,
I do not know.
But the ships that crawl
through the waves
look majestic.

My daddy works
    in the daytime
    and sleeps
    after the sun goes down
    at night.

But he tells me that
some animals sleep
in their dens
in the daytime

and find their food
at night.

You have planned everything,
God!
The animals on the land,
and the fish in the sea,

and the people

on the earth

wait for you, God!

The cold of the winter

and the warmness

of the summer

depend upon you, God!

Your laws control
the sun faraway
and make the earth
circle very fast.

I will sing to you always,
God.

I will praise you always,
God.

I will pray to you always,
God.

Printed in U.S.A.